Jessica Cassar

I ♡ LoLs!

WHAT'S INSIDE...

©MGA

I'VE GOT A HEART OF GOLD

THE RAREST OF THEM ALL!

Luxe
WANT ☐ OWN ☐

 LittleBrother

Published 2018. Little Brother Books Ltd, Ground Floor,
23 Southernhay East, Exeter, Devon, EX1 1QL
Printed in Poland
books@littlebrotherbooks.co.uk   www.littlebrotherbooks.co.uk
The Little Brother Books trademark, email, website addresses are
the sole and exclusive properties of Little Brother Books Limited.

 MGA ENTERTAINMENT

PEARL SURPRISE CLUB LOVES...

YOU'RE IN PEARL SURPRISE CLUB IF YOU LIKE...

Anything that glitters ☐
Precious jewels ☐
Hunting for treasure on the beach ☐

WHO'S IN PEARL SURPRISE CLUB?

Precious
WANT ☐   OWN ☑

Treasure
WANT ☑   OWN ☐

Lil Precious
WANT ☑   OWN ☑

Lil Treasure
WANT ☑   OWN ☐

ADD YOUR OWN PEARL SURPRISE CLUB PHRASE, HERE:

....

START YOUR OWN L.O.L. SURPRISE! CLUB

Take inspiration from Pearl Surprise Club and start your own secret club!

I CALL MY CLUB:

~~Chill Out Club~~ Splash club

MY CLUB STANDS FOR:

1. ~~chilling out~~ corl
2. swimng like a mermaid
3. diging treasure up on the beach

> THE WORLD IS MY OYSTER

WHO'S IN MY CLUB?

WRITE YOUR CLUB MEMBER NAMES HERE:

Treshre

splash Queen

merbaby

waves

OUR MOTTO IS:

OUR RULES ARE:

SWIM CLUB LOVES...

Q. WHAT WORD LOOKS THE SAME BACKWARDS WHEN IT'S TURNED UPSIDE DOWN?
A. SWIMS

FLOAT ON!

YOU'RE IN SWIM CLUB IF YOU LIKE...
Beaches ☐ Sunglasses ☐
Surfing ☐ Vacation ☐
Cool pool accessories ☐

WHO'S IN SWIM CLUB?

EAT. SLEEP. BEACH

DON'T BE SHADY, BE A BABY!

Rip Tide
WANT ☐ OWN ☐

Vacay Babay
WANT ☑ OWN ☑

Waves
WANT ☑ OWN ☐

SPF Q.T.
WANT ☐ OWN ☐

SEA U AT THE BEACH!

CATCH ME POOOLSIDE

FLOAT LYFE 4 EVA

Lil Rip Tide
WANT ☐ OWN ☐

Lil Vacay Babay
WANT ☑ OWN ☐

Lil Waves
WANT ☐ OWN ☐

Lil SPF Q.T.
WANT ☐ OWN ☐

ADD YOUR OWN SWIM CLUB PHRASE, HERE:

....

8

©MGA

STYLE IT UP

Vacay Babay loves a day at the beach with her Swim Club pals. Especially if there's a chance to style it out with a new look!

SPLASH-SENSATION!

GIVE THIS SWIMSUIT A CRAY-CRAY MAKEOVER.

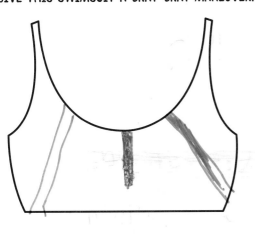

SHADY LADY

NOW FOR THE SHADES...

VACAY ALL DAY

BEACH-BLING READY!

A BEACH BAG FINISHES THE LOOK.

S.T.E.M. CLUB LOVES...

Q. HOW DID THE ASTRONAUT SERVE DINNER IN OUTER SPACE? A. ON FLYING SAUCERS.

ONE GIANT LEAP FOR BABYKIND!

YOU'RE IN S.T.E.M. CLUB IF YOU LIKE...

- Puzzles ☑
- Science ☑
- Computers ☑
- Rocket-launches ☑
- Engineering ☑
- Being smart! ☑

WHO'S IN S.T.E.M. CLUB?

IF IT AIN'T BROKE, DON'T FIX IT!

LAB IS FAB!

Can Do Baby
WANT ☐ OWN ☐

V.R.Q.T.
WANT ☑ OWN ☐

Glamstronaut
WANT ☑ OWN ☑

P.H.D.B.B.
WANT ☑ OWN ☐

TINY, BUT MIGHTY

Lil Can Do Baby
WANT ☐ OWN ☐

REALITY IS OVERRATED!

Lil V.R.Q.T.
WANT ☑ OWN ☐

Lil Glamstronaut
WANT ☑ OWN ☐

I GOT MY ION STYLE

Lil P.H.D.B.B.
WANT ☑ OWN ☐

CODIN' CUTIES

S.T.E.M. Club love to set cool challenges for each other.
Help them solve these tricky coding puzzles.

ANSWERS ON PAGE 77.

PASSWORD PICKER

CROSS OUT ALL THE LETTERS THAT APPEAR MORE THAN TWICE.
THEN UNSCRAMBLE THE CODE TO REVEAL THE WIFI PASSWORD.

R̶ Q̶
I̶
G̶ J̶ U̶ G̶ T̶ E A V̶ S̶
Q̶ A S̶ Q̶ G̶ T̶ J̶ T̶
T̶ P J̶ V̶ A R̶ V̶

The password is

E T P _ _ _ _ _ _

COOL CODE CHALLENGE

ARE THERE MORE ZEROS OR ONES IN THIS CODE?

1̶	0	1̶	1̶	1̶	0
1̶	1̶	0	1̶	0	1̶
0	1̶	0	0	1̶	0
1̶	1̶	0	1̶	1̶	0
1̶	0	0	0	1̶	0
0	1̶	0	0	1̶	1̶

There are more

.... ones ....

WHAT'S THE WIFI PASSWORD?

SPACED OUT

CIRCLE EVERY THIRD LETTER IN THIS CODE TO SEE WHAT V.R.Q.T. IS
LOOKING FORWARD TO. THE FIRST LETTER IS CIRCLED FOR YOU.

W E Ⓒ O R Ⓞ I U D Ⓤ Y I Ⓝ H N R
F G Ⓔ R P Y Ⓖ A I H R Ⓟ F Ⓐ Y T Ⓨ

coding party   Coding party

V.R.Q.T. IS LOOKING FORWARD TO A ..... coding party .....

11

SLEEPOVER CLUB LOVES...

YOU'RE IN SLEEPOVER CLUB IF YOU LIKE...

Parties ☑ Giggles ☑
Cosy pyjamas ☑
Quality time with BBF's! ☑

CURL UP AND NAP

WHO'S IN SLEEPOVER CLUB?

Babydoll
WANT ☐ OWN ☐

I'M SO WOKE

Snuggle Babe
WANT ☐ OWN ☑

Sleeping B.B.
WANT ☐ OWN ☐

ME + SNOOZE BUTTON = BFFS

Sleepy Bones
WANT ☐ OWN ☑

Lil Babydoll
WANT ☐ OWN ☑

I DREAM IN BLACK AND WHITE

Lil Snuggle Babe
WANT ☐ OWN ☐

Lil Sleeping B.B.
WANT ☐ OWN ☐

WAKING UP ON THE WRONG SIDE OF THE CRIB

Lil Sleepy Bones
WANT ☐ OWN ☐

©MGA

SLEEPOVER PARTY ESSENTIALS

The Sleepover Club plan their parties in advance, and throw in a few surprises for that L.O.L. feeling!

SLEEPOVER CLUB SCHEDULE

- 💜 **6pm** Welcome
- 💜 **6.30** Tell a sleepover story
- 💜 **7.00** pretend fashon show
- 💜 **7.30** Decorate your own cupcake
- 💜 **8.00** do each over's hair
- 💜 **8.30** Pampering session
- 💜 **9.00** Spa half-an-hour
- 💜 **9.30** Movie and popcorn
- 💜 **10.00** Lights out, night, night!

PLAN YOUR PERFECT SLEEPOVER PARTY, HERE. THE SLEEPOVER CLUB HAVE ADDED A FEW SURPRISE GAMES!

I NEED MY BEAUTY SLEEP!

13

©MGA

THEATER CLUB LOVES...

YOU'RE IN THEATER CLUB IF YOU LIKE...

Getting on stage ☐   Singing ☐
Making up stories ☐   Dancing ☐
Dressing up in costume ☐

U WISH!

WHO'S IN THEATER CLUB?

Angel
WANT ☑   OWN ☐

I BELIEVE IN MYSELF!

Unicorn
WANT ☑   OWN ☐

EMOJIS ARE THE NEW HIEROGLYPHICS

Pharaoh Babe
WANT ☐   OWN ☐

Coconut Q.T.
WANT ☑   OWN ☐

ALWAYS ACTING OUT!

Lil Angel
WANT ☐   OWN ☐

RAINBOW IS MY FAVORITE COLOR!

Lil Unicorn
WANT ☑   OWN ☐

Q. WHY DID THE GIRL PUT HER HEAD ON THE PIANO? A. SHE WANTED TO PLAY BY EAR!

MAHALO VERY MUCH!

Lil Coconut Q.T.
WANT ☐   OWN ☐

THE SHOW MUST GO ON!

The Theater Club girls are born to perform.
Take some tips and hold your own star search.

INVITE YOUR CLUB MEMBERS!

Send out invites for your talent show.
Remember, all guests should try to take part!

I'D RATHER BE SWIMMING

Invitation

Name.....Marren....Dunn.....................

....

You are invited to .....Jessica.....'s talent show!

On .....the 23rd of october.....................

At .....My....house.....................

Wear sparkles, and prepare to dazzle!

PRACTISE, PRACTISE, PRACTISE

No one ever got to steal the show
without hours and hours of preparation.

Try practising in front of a mirror to get
your performance show-ready.

Don't forget a dress rehearsal too -
you want to wow your audience
with a show-stopping look!

THE BIG REVEAL

It's time for the show, and your chance to shine. Remember, everyone gets nervous, but make like the Theater club girls, and grin until you're winning!

Take it in turns to introduce each act, and make each one sound amazing, marvellous, and totally show-stopping.

Keep a score card for each performer.

Score Card

OUTFIT	
PERFORMANCE	
OVERALL SCORE	

THE WINNER IS...

Make a trophy to give to your winner. Trace this one, cut it out and decorate it with a Theater Club twist.

Performing is the best fun!

WINNER!

©MGA

BIG SURPRISE CLUB LOVES...

YOU'RE IN BIG SURPRISE CLUB IF YOU LIKE...

Secret clubs ☐
Anything exclusive or rare ☐
Guessing games! ☐

U DON'T GOTTA B COOL 2 RULE MY WORLD

WHO'S IN BIG SURPRISE CLUB?

Purple Queen
WANT ☑ OWN ☑

GROUND CONTROL TO MAJOR B.B.

Stardust Queen
WANT ☑ OWN ☑

Lil Purple Queen
WANT ☐ OWN ☑

I'M THE BABE WITH THE POWER

Lil Stardust Queen
WANT ☑ OWN ☑

PLAY L.O.L. WHO AM I?

Surprise girls love the thrill of a guessing game...
here's how to have your own surprise fun.

INSTRUCTIONS

1 Each player takes a sticky note, and writes down the name of an L.O.L. Surprise! character.

2 Each person sticks their sticky note on to someone else's forehead (without the other player seeing).

3 Players take it in turns to guess their character, by asking the other players questions. Each player gets 30 seconds to guess.

4 The other players can only answer yes or no.

5 The first person to guess correctly is the **L.O.L. Surprise! queen.**

PARTY LIKE IT'S 9.59PM!

STARDUST QUEEN

LIL STARDUST QUEEN

19

©MGA

DANCE CLUB LOVES...

Q. WHY DO ANTS DANCE ON JAM JARS? A. BECAUSE IT SAYS: TWIST TO OPEN!

STEPPIN' OUT!

YOU'RE IN DANCE CLUB IF YOU LIKE...

Dance tutorials ☐   Swing dance ☐
Going to discos ☐   Ballet ☐
Watching pop videos ☐

WHO'S IN DANCE CLUB?

TUTU CUTE!

Center Stage
WANT ☑   OWN ☐

Line Dancer
WANT ☐   OWN ☐

Sis Swing
WANT ☑   OWN ☐

SPOTLIGHT ON ME!

Lil Center Stage
WANT ☐   OWN ☐

JUST A SMALL TOWN BABY

Lil Line Dancer
WANT ☐   OWN ☐

Lil Sis Swing
WANT ☐   OWN ☐

©MGA

DANCE DIVAS

Grab your signature move, get a Dance club makeover, then groove the night away. The Dance Club girls are rooting for you!

DON'T BE A SQUARE

DANCE MOVE PICKER

Look at the words in box one. Now close your eyes. Open them, and pick the first word you are drawn to.

Repeat for the second box of words. Put the words together and you have your new dance move invention!

BOX 1

GRACEFUL

FLOATY

ROCKIN'

SHIMMY

SCOOCHY

BOX 2

SCOOPER

WINDMILL

CHICKEN STEP

ARABESQUE

SPLITS

MY DANCE MOVE IS THE _Rockin'_ _Splits_

GLAM CLUB LOVES...

YOU'RE IN GLAM CLUB IF YOU LIKE...

Makeovers ☐ Hair tutorials ☐
Accessorising to the max! ☐
Fashion shows ☐
Standing up for style! ☐

ALWAYS READY FOR MY SELFIE

WHO'S IN GLAM CLUB?

IT'S SHOWTIME!

I DON'T DO GLAM, I AM GLAM

Showbaby
WANT ☐ OWN ☑

Black Tie
WANT ☐ OWN ☐

Flower Child
WANT ☑ OWN ☐

It Baby
WANT ☐ OWN ☐

SHOWBIZ IS MY BIZ

PICK ME, PICK ME!

TRES CHIC!

Lil Showbaby
WANT ☐ OWN ☐

Lil Black Tie
WANT ☐ OWN ☐

Lil Flower Child
WANT ☐ OWN ☐

Lil It Baby
WANT ☐ OWN ☐

ADD YOUR OWN GLAM CLUB PHRASE, HERE:

....

Royal High-Ney
WANT ☐ OWN ☐

Leading Baby
WANT ☐ OWN ☐

Miss Punk
WANT ☐ OWN ☐

Dollface
WANT ☐ OWN ☐

Miss Baby
WANT ☐ OWN ☐

Lil Miss Punk
WANT ☐ OWN ☐

Lil Dollface
WANT ☐ OWN ☐

Lil Miss Baby
WANT ☐ OWN ☐

©MGA

BOW BEAUTIFUL

Glam Club girls love to accessorise to the max! Give these gifts the most glamour-iffic makeover you can imagine!

BLING IT ON

Colour each box a different colour, and add cool patterns to the bows.

ADD YOUR OWN BOW!

PUT A SASH ON IT!

GLAM CLUB GIRL TIP:
Next time you give a gift, why not make your own wrapping paper? Give it a surprise twist by adding in more than one layer of paper. Put a message in each layer. It makes unboxing so much more glam!

GLITTERATI CLUB LOVES...

WHAT'S THE BUZZ, HONEY?

YOU'RE IN GLITTERATI CLUB IF YOU LIKE...

Being fabulous! ☐ Selfies ☐
Anything sparkly ☐
Making a grand entrance! ☐
Glitter, glitter, and more glitter! ☐

WHO'S IN GLITTERATI CLUB?

CAUTION, GLITTER AHEAD!

YOU BETTA WERK!

Independent Queen
WANT ☑ OWN ☑

Goo-Goo Queen
WANT ☐ OWN ☐

Boss Queen
WANT ☐ OWN ☐

Madame Queen
WANT ☐ OWN ☐

Lil Independent Queen
WANT ☐ OWN ☐

WHEN ALL ELSE FAILS...SPRINKLE GLITTER ON IT!

I ONLY TAKE POWER NAPS

Lil Boss Queen
WANT ☐ OWN ☐

YES, ON PROPZZZ

Lil Madame Queen
WANT ☐ OWN ☐

26

©MGA

MAKE GLITTERATI SLIME!

The Glitterati Club girls love to experiment with glittery, new ideas! Try this glitter slime for goo with a sparkly difference!

STARS. STRIPES. SPARKLES. SASS.

WARNING! ADULT GUIDANCE IS NEEDED FOR THIS ACTIVITY.

INGREDIENTS

140ml/5 fl oz of clear, non-toxic glue

140ml/5 fl oz of warm water

1/2 teaspoon of baking soda

Pots of coloured glitter (preferably biodegradable)

A few squirts of contact lens solution

Clean plastic pot with sealable lid

©MGA

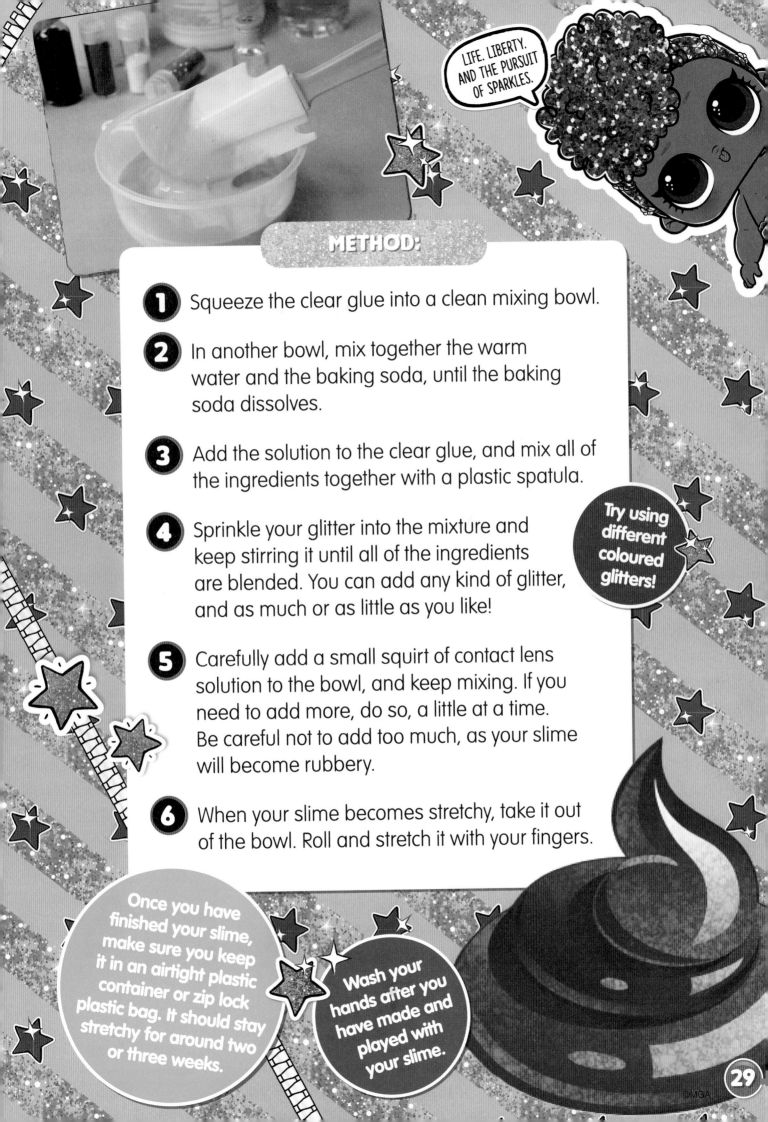

LIFE, LIBERTY, AND THE PURSUIT OF SPARKLES.

METHOD:

1 Squeeze the clear glue into a clean mixing bowl.

2 In another bowl, mix together the warm water and the baking soda, until the baking soda dissolves.

3 Add the solution to the clear glue, and mix all of the ingredients together with a plastic spatula.

4 Sprinkle your glitter into the mixture and keep stirring it until all of the ingredients are blended. You can add any kind of glitter, and as much or as little as you like!

Try using different coloured glitters!

5 Carefully add a small squirt of contact lens solution to the bowl, and keep mixing. If you need to add more, do so, a little at a time. Be careful not to add too much, as your slime will become rubbery.

6 When your slime becomes stretchy, take it out of the bowl. Roll and stretch it with your fingers.

Once you have finished your slime, make sure you keep it in an airtight plastic container or zip lock plastic bag. It should stay stretchy for around two or three weeks.

Wash your hands after you have made and played with your slime.

29

©MGA

OPPOSITES CLUB LOVES...

YOU'RE IN OPPOSITES CLUB IF YOU LIKE...

Contrasting colours ☐   Sweet 'n' salty treats ☐
Celebrating the differences in everything! ☐
Seeing the other side of the story ☐
Always being fair to everyone! ☐

HOT LIKE A PEPPER!

WHO'S IN OPPOSITES CLUB?

RISE AND SHINE!

Dawn
WANT ☑   OWN ☑

I'M NOT A MORNING PERSON...

Dusk
WANT ☑   OWN ☐

Sugar
WANT ☑   OWN ☐

Spice
WANT ☑   OWN ☐

WAKE ME UP B4 YOU GOO-GOO!

Lil Dawn
WANT ☑   OWN ☐

Lil Dusk
WANT ☑   OWN ☐

AGREE TO DISAGREE!

Lil Sugar
WANT ☑   OWN ☐

TWO WRONGS MAKE A RIGHT!

Lil Spice
WANT ☑   OWN ☐

Q. WHAT GETS LONGER AS THE DAY GETS SHORTER? A. A SHADOW.

MORE ISSUES THAN *VOGUE*

CHILL OUT AND UNSUBSCRIBE

SWEET AS CANDY!

Fancy
WANT ☑ OWN ☐

Fresh
WANT ☑ OWN ☐

ALWAYS LOOK YOUR BEST

Lil Fancy
WANT ☑ OWN ☐

Lil Fresh
WANT ☑ OWN ☐

CREATE YOUR OWN OPPOSITE!

Pick out the opposites that appeal to you, to make a new L.O.L. character.

Sweet
Cute
Fiery
Night

Cheeky
'N' Sour
Day
Calm

I created

Cute   Calm

31

©MGA

NAIL IT!

Opposite Club girls love to show their true colours with a mis-matched nail makeover. The crazier, the better!

RISE AND SHINE!

❤ INSTRUCTIONS ❤

1 Gather all of your favourite nail polishes.

2 Carefully paint each nail a different colour.

3 Leave to dry.

4 Your Opposites Club nail art is good to go!

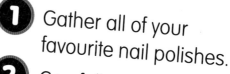

WAKE ME UP B4 YOU GOO-GOO!

©MGA

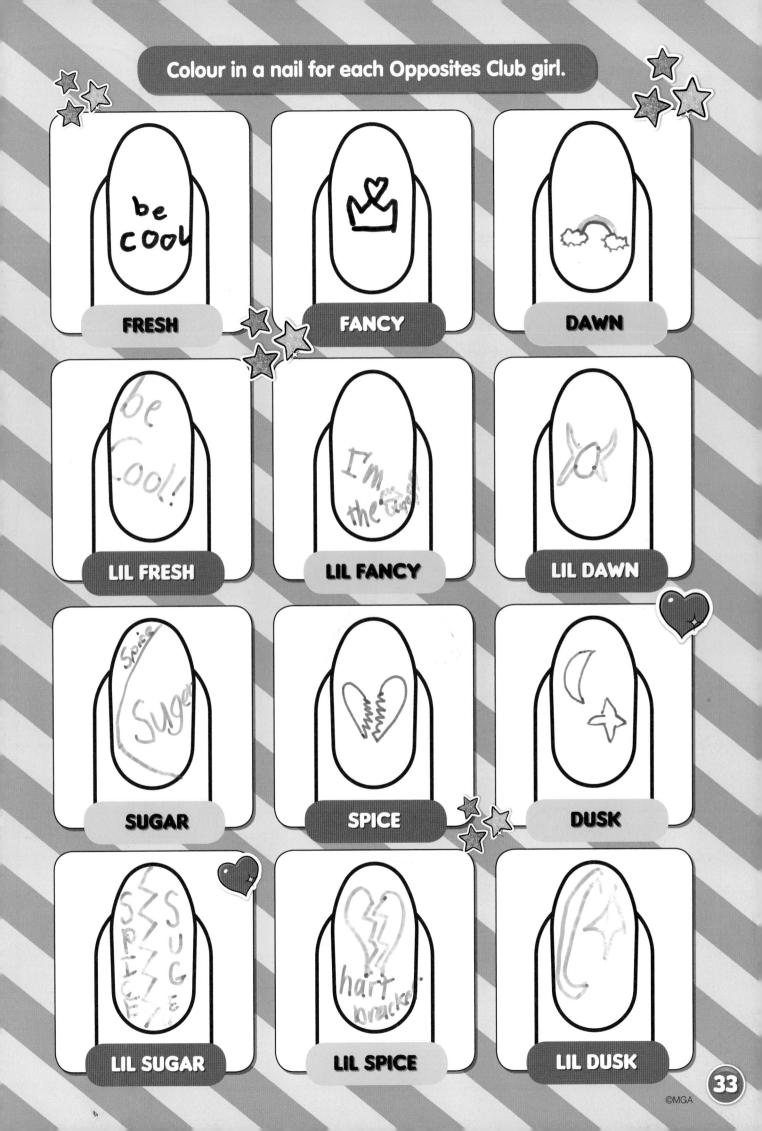

HIP HOP CLUB LOVES...

SHORTY-LICIOUS FOR YA, BABE!

YOU'RE A HIP HOP CLUB GIRL IF YOU LIKE...

Big beats ☐ Rhythm and rhyme ☐
Expressing yourself through music ☐
Styling it out with cool trainers and sportswear ☐

WHO'S IN HIP HOP CLUB?

WORK IT B.B.

D.J.
WANT ☑ OWN ☐

Shorty
WANT ☑ OWN ☐

Honey Bun
WANT ☐ OWN ☐

Beats
WANT ☑ OWN ☐

SPINNIN' AND GRINNIN'

Lil D.J.
WANT ☑ OWN ☐

SHORTY FROM THE TOY BLOCKS!

Lil Shorty
WANT ☑ OWN ☐

HUG LIFE!

Lil Honey Bun
WANT ☐ OWN ☐

I DON'T WANT NO NAPS!

Lil Beats
WANT ☐ OWN ☐

ADD YOUR OWN HIP HOP CLUB PHRASE, HERE:

....

WORD UP

Try writing your own hip hop lyrics.
When you've finished, rap them to a big beat!

Cool cool cool cool
beat beat beat beat
Swag Swag Swag

CRAZYSLEEPYCOOL

HIP HOP CHALLENGE!

When it comes to games, Hip Hop Club are top players!
Play this chatterbox game and style it out... your way.

INSTRUCTIONS

1 Trace the chatterbox template on to a piece of paper.

2 Place the piece of paper face down, and fold each corner into the middle of the square.

3 Turn the paper over and repeat on the other side.

4 Fold the paper in half to make a rectangle, then again to make a square.

5 Slide your fingers and thumbs under the coloured circles to open out the chatterbox.

TO PLAY

Each player chooses a colour. Open and close the squares as you spell it out.

Each player then chooses a Hip Hop Club character. Open the flap to discover the challenge!

TOP KNOT, TOP NOTCH!

TODAY I WILL BE WEARING...

_____

_____

_____

TODAY I WILL BE ACTING LIKE...

_____

_____

_____

TODAY I WILL BE CREATIVE BECAUSE...

_____

_____

_____

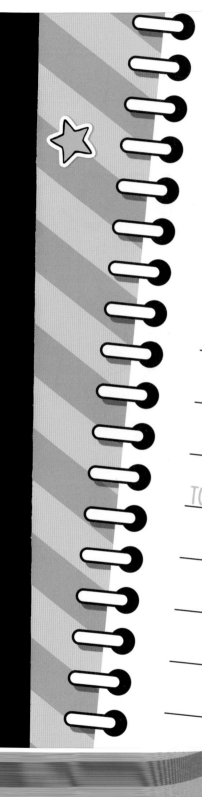

BE INSPIRED

FASHION DESIGNERS HAVE A LOOK BOOK TO HELP THEM CREATE BRILLIANT IDEAS. MAKE YOUR OWN HERE.

I WANT IT ALL!

THINK OF A MUSE

Pick your favourite L.O.L. Surprise! doll to be your muse. Write one word that sums her up.

MY FAVE L.O.L. SURPRISE! DOLL IS ____Glashrat____

MY WORD IS ____Space____

This word is now the theme for your look book.

A MUSE IS A PERSON WHO IS INSPIRATIONAL TO A DESIGNER'S LOOK.

GET COLLECTING

Now collect anything and everything you can find about your theme and stick it below. You could use...

OLD TICKETS   PACKAGING   PHOTOS   PICTURES FROM MAGAZINES   SCRAPS OF FABRIC

Bon Bo

OWN

LOOK AGAIN

Look at what you've collected. What do you like about the shapes, colours and patterns in your collection? Experiment by drawing different details in these boxes.

GET SKETCHING

Now draw your muse in a funky outfit. Colour the outfit in, or cut up paper and make a collage design.

MY OUTFIT IS CALLED: _a Splash of Neon_

STORYBOOK CLUB LOVES...

NEW WORLD. WHO DIS?

YOU'RE IN STORYBOOK CLUB IF YOU LIKE...

Reading ☐ Writing ☐
Exploring your imagination ☐

Q. WHAT DO YOU GET IF YOU THROW A MILLION BOOKS INTO THE SEA?
A. A TITLE WAVE!

WHO'S IN STORYBOOK CLUB?

Curious Q.T.
WANT ☑ OWN ☑

Heartbreaker
WANT ☐ OWN ☑

PEEK A BOO

Hops
WANT ☑ OWN ☐

Troublemaker
WANT ☑ OWN ☐

Lil Curious Q.T.
WANT ☐ OWN ☐

FINGERPAINTING THE ROSES RED

Lil Heartbreaker
WANT ☐ OWN ☐

Lil Hops
WANT ☐ OWN ☐

Lil Troublemaker
WANT ☐ OWN ☐

©MGA

SURPRISE STORY

1. Grab two friends, a piece of paper and a pen.

2. The youngest writes the beginning of a story, then folds over the paper so no one else can see what they've written. They then write a sentence to start the middle of the story. They pass the paper to the person on their left.

3. The next player writes the middle of the story, folds the paper over so it can't be read, then writes a sentence to start the end of the story. They then pass it to the person on their left.

4. The final player writes the end of the story. Then they open the paper and read the whole story out.

Now turn over the page, for ideas on how to illustrate your story!

MAKE IT AS SILLY AND FUNNY AS YOU LIKE.

SKETCH IT OUT

BRING YOUR STORIES TO LIFE BY DRAWING YOUR CHARACTERS.

First, practise your drawing skills by drawing the other half of Lil Troublemaker.

GET DRAWING

Now draw a character for the story you created on the previous page.

BREAKIN' HEARTS AND TAKIN' NAMES!

Write down everything you can think of for your character.

NAME: _____

AGE: _____

LOVES: _____

CAN'T STAND: _____

THEIR FAVOURITE SURPRISE WOULD BE:

_____

STORYTIME!

Now draw the rest of your characters here.

OUR IMAGINATIONS SET US FREE!

45

CHILLOUT CLUB LOVES...

ALWAYS CLASSY AND A LIL SASSY!

YOU'RE IN CHILLOUT CLUB IF YOU LIKE...

Being totally cool about everything ☐
Getting cosy ☐   Just chillin' ☐
Hanging out with friends ☐

WHO'S IN CHILLOUT CLUB?

Cozy Babe
WANT ☐ OWN ☐

PUMPKIN SPICE EVERYTHING!

Snow Angel
WANT ☑ OWN ☐

Brrr B.B.
WANT ☑ OWN ☑

Posh
WANT ☑ OWN ☐

Lil Cozy Babe
WANT ☐ OWN ☐

SNOW BALL FIGHT!

Lil Snow Angel
WANT ☐ OWN ☐

Lil Brrr B.B.
WANT ☑ OWN ☐

Lil Posh
WANT ☐ OWN ☐

MAKE A CHILLED-OUT MEME

SIMPLY ADD A FUNNY CAPTION LIKE 'I WOKE UP LIKE THIS!" TO THIS PICTURE OF LIL POSH.

Q. WHY DID THE GIRL PUT HER GUITAR IN THE FRIDGE? A. BECAUSE SHE LIKED COOL MUSIC!

SURPRISE PAMPERING SESSION

THE CHILL OUT CLUB LOVE GETTING PAMPERED. INVITE YOUR FRIENDS ROUND, THEN SURPRISE THEM WITH THESE SPA RECIPES!

FOOT AND HAND SCRUB

THE BODY SCRUB WILL KEEP FOR ONE WEEK.

YOU WILL NEED...

- 1 CUP SUGAR ☑
- 1 CUP HONEY ☑
- 1 TEASPOON STRAWBERRY EXTRACT ☑
- ½ TEASPOON VANILLA EXTRACT ☑
- 3 TABLESPOONS BABY OIL ☑
- PINK FOOD COLOURING ☑
- 1 SMALL JAR OR CONTAINER WITH LID ☑

HOW TO MAKE:

1. In a mixing bowl, add sugar, honey, baby oil, strawberry and vanilla extract. Mix together well until all ingredients are blended.

2. Add a small amount of pink food colouring and stir.

3. Add the mixture to a jar or container.

HOW TO USE

Massage slowly into feet and hands, then rinse with warm water. Make sure you have a towel handy to dry off.

TOP TIP

Add a slice of cucumber to each eye while you rub in the foot and hand scrub to make the pampering extra-relaxing!

YOU WILL NEED...

- 7 WOODEN SKEWERS ✓
- 7 RASPBERRIES ✓
- 7 HULLED STRAWBERRIES ✓
- 7 TANGERINE SEGMENTS ✓
- 7 CUBES PEELED MANGO ✓
- 7 PEELED PINEAPPLE CHUNKS ✓
- 7 PEELED KIWI FRUIT CHUNKS ✓
- 7 GREEN GRAPES ✓
- 7 RED GRAPES ✓
- 14 BLUEBERRIES ✓

ARE YOU 'COOL' ENOUGH TO JOIN US?

RAINBOW FRUIT KEBABS

HOW TO MAKE:

1 Take 7 wooden skewers and thread the following fruit onto each – 1 raspberry, 1 strawberry, 1 tangerine segment, 1 cube of peeled mango, 1 chunk of peeled pineapple, 1 chunk of peeled kiwi, 1 green and 1 red grape, and finish off with 2 blueberries.

2 Arrange in a rainbow shape and let everyone help themselves.

CHILLIN' WITH MY HOMIES!

PLEASE ASK A GROWN-UP FOR HELP BEFORE USING SHARP KNIVES.

WE LOVE TO CHILL TOGETHER

TOP TIP

If you have any leftover fruit, pop it into a blender, add some milk and make a delicious and oh-so-nutritious smoothie.

RETRO CLUB LOVES...

OUTTA SIGHT, BB!

YOU'RE IN RETRO CLUB IF YOU LIKE...

Record players ☐
Partying like it's 1999 ☐
Amusement arcades ☐
Vintage style ☐

Q. WHAT DO YOU CALL AN INSECT DANCING AT A RETRO DISCO? A. A JITTERBUG!

WHO'S IN RETRO CLUB?

Beatnik Babe
WANT ☐ OWN ☐

Foxy
WANT ☑ OWN ☐

PEACE. LOVE. SURPRISES.

Go-Go Gurl ✓
WANT ☐ OWN ☑

Jitterbug
WANT ☐ OWN ☐

Lil Beatnik Babe
WANT ☐ OWN ☐

Lil Foxy
WANT ☐ OWN ☐

FAR OUT!

Lil Go-Go Gurl
WANT ☐ OWN ☐

Lil Jitterbug
WANT ☐ OWN ☐

50 ©MGA

Cherry
WANT ☑ OWN ☐

BABY SCHOOL DROP OUT.

Pink Baby
WANT ☐ OWN ☐

B.B. Bop
WANT ☐ OWN ☐

PIN-UP THAT DIAPER

Lil Cherry
WANT ☐ OWN ☐

Lil Pink Baby
WANT ☐ OWN ☐

I CAN HELP!

Lil B.B. Bop
WANT ☐ OWN ☐

DELICIOUS DOODLES

Add some colour to these old-fashioned sweets.

CREATE A TIME CAPSULE

THAT'S WILD!

MAKE A TIME CAPSULE ALL ABOUT YOU AND EVERYTHING YOU LOVE. THEN SET A DATE IN THE FUTURE TO GET TOGETHER WITH YOUR FRIENDS AND FAMILY TO OPEN IT UP AND SURPRISE YOUR FUTURE SELF!

HOW TO MAKE:

1 Find a metal biscuit tin and line it with tissue paper so all your treasures are protected.

2 Collect everything on the check list and carefully put it all in the tin.

3 Add some extra things that are special to you like stickers or posters.

4 Seal the tin and bury it!

TOP TIP

DON'T PUT ANYTHING IN THAT WILL GO MOULDY! YUCK!

CHECK LIST

- PHOTOS OF YOU, YOUR FRIENDS AND FAMILY ☐
- AN MP3 OF YOUR FAVOURITE SONGS ☐
- A PICTURE OF YOUR FAVOURITE OUTFIT ☐
- THE FRONT PAGE OF TODAY'S NEWSPAPER ☐
- THE LATEST ISSUE OF YOUR FAVOURITE MAGAZINE ☐
- YOUR FAVOURITE BOOK ☐
- YOUR FILLED-IN QUESTIONNAIRE ☐
- A MESSAGE FOR THE FUTURE YOU ☐

LET ME DO IT!

WE ARE GOING TO OPEN THE TIME CAPSULE ON:

SIGNED_____

DATE_____

EXCITED YET?

QUESTIONNAIRE

Fill this out and see if it has come true when you open your time capsule!

NAME _____ DATE _____

WHEN I GROW UP MY JOB WILL BE _____

I DEFINITELY WON'T BE _____

I'LL LIVE IN _____

53

SPIRIT CLUB LOVES...

Q. WHY DON'T DOGS MAKE GOOD DANCERS? A. BECAUSE THEY HAVE TWO LEFT FEET!

GAGA FOR RA-RA!

YOU'RE IN SPIRIT CLUB IF YOU LIKE...

Cheering on your friends ☑
Teamwork ☑   Being on the go ☑
Having tons of energy ☐

WHO'S IN SPIRIT CLUB?

STRAIGHT A'S 4 EVA

Majorette
WANT ☐ OWN ☐

Teacher's Pet
WANT ☐ OWN ☐

Cheer Captain
WANT ☐ OWN ☐

LET'S GET IN FORMATION

BORN TO LEARN!

Lil Majorette
WANT ☐ OWN ☐

Lil Teacher's Pet
WANT ☐ OWN ☐

Lil Cheer Captain
WANT ☐ OWN ☐

WORD WHIZZ

Can you spot the words hidden in this word search?

ANSWERS ON PAGE 77

CHEER   CLAP   DANCE   FRIENDS

```
U P R S R P C E C D
C N E F D O C L U V
I H E E X N P G A O
L H H K A Q E V R P
B J C D S V D I X H
T P W F U Q Y C R F
H L J F D P B Y S F
P B A I G Q B H Q B
C H A N T N A E N C
T Y L U K C X T O S
```

TEAMWORK MAKES THE DREAMWORK!

HIDDEN SURPRISE

There's an extra word that's not on the list hidden in the wordsearch. Can you find it?

THE SURPRISE WORD IS:

55

©MGA

MAKE CHEERLEADER POM POMS

YOU CAN MAKE THESE GORGEOUS POM POMS IN MINUTES!

WARNING! ADULT GUIDANCE IS NEEDED FOR THIS ACTIVITY.

YOU WILL NEED...

10 X BRIGHT TISSUE PAPER SHEETS

PINKING SHEARS

BRIGHT TAPE

FOLLOW MY LEAD!

TOP TIP

You could add glitter to your pom poms too.

HOW TO MAKE...

1 Make a pile of all the tissue papers.

2 Fold the tissue paper in half.

3 Using your pinking shears to create zig-zag lines, cut thick strips all along the length of the paper. Leave a couple of centimetres at the top uncut.

4 Roll the uncut sections of tissue paper tightly to make the handles for your pom poms.

5 Stick some bright tape around the handles.

©MGA

HOW TO MAKE UP A CHEER

MAKE UP A SURPRISE CHANT FOR YOUR BFF USING INFORMATION LIKE HER NAME, HER FAVORITE COLOUR, MOVIE – WHATEVER YOU LIKE.

WRITE YOUR SURPRISE CHANT HERE :

GIVE ME AN S.P.I.R.I.T.

57

GLITTER CLUB LOVES...

BAM! POW! SPARKLE!

YOU'RE IN GLITTER CLUB IF YOU LIKE...

Surprise parties ☐   All that glitters! ☐

Spur of the moment fun ☐

WHO'S IN GLITTER SERIES?

Super B.B.
WANT ☐ OWN ☐

Center Stage
WANT ☐ OWN ☐

Miss Baby
WANT ☐ OWN ☐

GLITTER FOR DAYS!

Queen Bee
WANT ☐ OWN ☐

I'M YOUR LUCKY STAR!

Cosmic Queen
WANT ☐ OWN ☐

Fancy
WANT ☐ OWN ☐

TOO MUCH GLITTER? I CAN'T EVEN...

Fresh
WANT ☐ OWN ☐

Teacher's Pet
WANT ☐ OWN ☐

Rocker
WANT ☐ OWN ☐

Diva
WANT ☐ OWN ☐

BORN TO SPARKLE!

M.C. Swag
WANT ☐ OWN ☐

I DON'T SWEAT, I SPARKLE

Hoops MVP
WANT ☐ OWN ☐

SPARKLY SWIRL

HOW MANY WORDS YOU CAN SPOT IN THE WHEEL?
TICK EACH ONE OFF THE LIST AS YOU FIND IT.

BEE YOUR SPARKLY SELF

ANSWERS ON PAGE 77

GLITTER ☑ SPARKLE ☑ SHIMMERY ☑ SHINE ☑
BRIGHT ☑ TWINKLE ☑ STAR ☑

©MGA

SURPRISE CUPCAKES

TWINKLE TWINKLE BABY!

INGREDIENTS

2 ½ CUPS PLAIN FLOUR	☐	1 CUP WHITE SUGAR	☐
2 TABLESPOONS BAKING POWDER	☐	3 EGGS	☐
½ TEASPOON BAKING SODA	☐	RED FOOD COLOURING	☐
½ TEASPOON OF SALT	☐	BLUE FOOD COLOURING	☐
½ CUP OF MILK	☐	GREEN GOOD COLOURING	☐
½ CUP OF VEGETABLE OIL	☐	YELLOW FOOD COLOURING	☐
1 TEASPOON VANILLA EXTRACT	☐	EDIBLE GLITTER (AVAILABLE FROM CAKE DECORATING SHOPS AND MOST BIG SUPERMARKETS)	☐
½ CUP BUTTER	☐		

HOW TO MAKE SURPRISE RAINBOW CAKES

1 Pre-heat an oven to 350 degrees F (175 degrees).

2 Line two 12 cup muffin pans with paper baking cups.

3 Stir together the flour, baking powder, baking soda, and salt in a large bowl until evenly blended. Set aside.

4 Whisk together the milk, vegetable oil and vanilla extract in a separate bowl. Set aside.

5 Beat the butter and sugar with an electric mixer in a large bowl until lighter in colour.

6 Add the eggs, one at a time.

7 Pour in the flour mixture alternately with the milk mixture, stirring lightly.

8 Add in lots of edible glitter and stir it in.

9 Divide the cake batter into four different bowls.

10 Add a few drops of food colouring into one bowl of batter and stir. Repeat with the remaining colours and bowls of batter.

11 Using a different spoon for each colour batter, spoon a small spoonful of each colour into the cupcake liners, until ¾ full. Don't mix it together!

12 Bake in the pre-heated oven for about 15-20 mins.

13 Leave to cool and decorate with sprinkles.

THESE BOOTS WERE MADE FOR ROCKIN'

©MGA

GLEE CLUB LOVES...

Q. WHAT SONG DO VAMPIRES HATE? A. YOU ARE MY SUNSHINE!

STRAIGHT OUTTA DAYCARE

YOU'RE IN GLEE CLUB IF YOU LIKE...

Singing ☐   Rocking out ☐

Forming a band with your friends ☐

WHO'S IN GLEE CLUB?

BORN THIS WAY!

Rocker
WANT ☑   OWN ☐

Diva
WANT ☐   OWN ☐

M.C. Swag
WANT ☑   OWN ☑

ROCK ON

Lil Rocker
WANT ☐   OWN ☐

SLAY ALL DAY!

Lil Diva
WANT ☐   OWN ☐

Lil M.C. Swag
WANT ☐   OWN ☐

WHICH SONG SHOULD YOU LEARN NEXT?

SHUT YOUR EYES AND HOLD YOUR HAND OVER THE BOX BELOW. POINT YOUR RIGHT INDEX FINGER AND DRAW A CIRCLE IN THE AIR THREE TIMES. NOW LET IT DROP. WHICHEVER SONG IT LANDS ON IS WHAT YOU SHOULD LEARN NEXT.

③ NO EXCUSES: MEGHAN TRAINOR

① WANNABE: THE SPICE GIRLS

② FIREWORK: KATY PERRY

ATHLETIC CLUB LOVES...

4 SHORE

YOU'RE IN ATHLETIC CLUB IF YOU LIKE...

Being part of a team ☐
Sports ☐ Going the extra mile ☐
Getting out and going for it ☐

WHO'S IN ATHLETIC CLUB?

Short Stop
WANT ☐ OWN ☐

YOU BETTA NOT DROP THE BALL

Spike
WANT ☐ OWN ☐

Touchdown
WANT ☐ OWN ☐

Sprints
WANT ☐ OWN ☐

Lil Short Stop
WANT ☐ OWN ☐

Q. WHAT KIND OF RACE IS NEVER RUN?
A. A SWIMMING RACE

HALF TIME. NAP TIME

Lil Touchdown
WANT ☐ OWN ☐

Lil Sprints
WANT ☐ OWN ☐

QUEEN OF THE RINK

Ice Sk8er
WANT ☑ OWN ☐

Kicks
WANT ☑ OWN ☐

Court Champ
WANT ☑ OWN ☑

Surfer Babe
WANT ☑ OWN ☐

Lil Ice Sk8er
WANT ☑ OWN ☐

SCORE!
Lil Kicks
WANT ☑ OWN ☐

Lil Court Champ
WANT ☑ OWN ☐

Lil Surfer Babe
WANT ☑ OWN ☐

I GOT GAME!

Hoops MVP
WANT ☐ OWN ☐

Roller Sk8ter
WANT ☐ OWN ☐

Lil Hoops MVP
WANT ☐ OWN ☐

Lil Roller Sk8ter
WANT ☐ OWN ☐

65

©MGA

FIND THE WORDS

CAN YOU SPOT THE ACTIVITIES HIDDEN IN THIS WORDSEARCH?

```
G N O Y I X W T X L J X U
C N Z W Q N Z G T S B D V
I X I V D K W R U M X C G
V R N M I A G N G B O N X
G Z K F M W F G N X R Z V
O G S D F I N V I U Z X L
W Z E Z P I W G P K O L Z
M Q H N N A Z S P U Q E F
H A L N F Y C E I I A A O
G J U V V O K E K T C W I
T R K C Q X Q N S H N M X
N Z B V F Y D Q R V V X Z
V J U F X E T J I F U G E
```

SK8, DON'T HATE!

GOOOOOOAL!

ANSWERS ON PAGE 77

HIDDEN SURPRISE

One of the words on the list is missing from the wordsearch. Which one is it?

THE MISSING WORD IS:

_____

66
©MGA

SPORTY TREASURE HUNT

COMPLETE EACH OF THE ACTIVITIES BELOW TO PICK UP A SYMBOL, THEN
UNSCRAMBLE THE SYMBOLS FOR A SURPRISE CHALLENGE. READY? STEADY? GO!

1 Hop on one leg
WELL DONE! YOUR SYMBOL IS A ☘ — T ☐

2 Run on the spot for 30 seconds
WELL DONE! YOUR SYMBOL IS A 🐚 — O ☐

3 Crawl like a bear across the room
WELL DONE! YOUR SYMBOL IS A 😎 — B ☐

4 Do 20 squats
WELL DONE! YOUR SYMBOL IS A 🚗 — f ☐

5 Do a crazy dance
WELL DONE! YOUR SYMBOL IS A 👑 — L ☐

6 Do 15 jumping jacks
WELL DONE! YOUR SYMBOL IS A 🐚 — O ☐

7 Challenge someone to a pillow fight
WELL DONE! YOUR SYMBOL IS A 💎 — a ☐

8 Punch your arms in front of you for 1 minute
WELL DONE! YOUR SYMBOL IS A 👑 — L ☐

KEY

USE THIS KEY
TO HELP YOU CRACK
THE SECRET CHALLENGE:

A = 💎   N = 🏫
B = 😎   O = 🐚
C = 💣   P = 🍭
D = 🐼   Q = 🐰
E = 👖   R = 🎮
F = 🚗   S = 🥔
G = 💡   T = ☘
H = 👗   U = ❤
I = ❄   V = 🌀
J = 🐱   W = 👸
K = 🛋   X = 🏀
L = 👑   Y = 😈
M = 🎭   Z = ⭐

SURPRISE CHALLENGE

YOUR SURPRISE CHALLENGE IS TO SET UP A GAME OF

T o b f l o a L WITH YOUR FRIENDS

67

ROCK CLUB LOVES...

LET'S RIOT!

YOU'RE IN ROCK CLUB IF YOU LIKE...

- Metallic colours ☑
- Loud music ☑
- Playing instruments ☑
- Rocking out! ☑

Q. WHAT MAKES MUSIC ON YOUR HEAD? A. A HAIR BAND!

WHO'S IN ROCK CLUB?

Grunge Grrrl
WANT ☐ OWN ☐

let's rock

Punk Boi
WANT ☑ OWN ☐

THAT'S SO FUNKADELIC!

Funky Q.T.
WANT ☐ OWN ☐

Cheeky Babe
WANT ☑ OWN ☐

Lil Grunge Grrrl
WANT ☐ OWN ☐

OI! OI!

Lil Punk Boi
WANT ☐ OWN ☐

Lil Funky Q.T.
WANT ☐ OWN ☐

Lil Cheeky Babe
WANT ☐ OWN ☐

©MGA

WHICH INSTRUMENT SHOULD YOU PLAY?

1 Write your full name here

Jessica Abbie Cassar

2 Under each letter, write down how many times that letter shows up in:

MUSICAL INSTRUMENTS

4 2 2 4

MY NUMBERS ADD UP TO:

12+

IF YOU SCORED...

0-5	6-11	12+
You should rock out on the guitar.	You'd be a natural on the drums.	The piano is totally your style.

HOW TO ROCK AT EVERYTHING

GIVE THINGS A TRY

IF YOU WANT TO TRY A NEW ACTIVITY, GO FOR IT. ASK YOURSELF, WHAT'S THE WORST THAT COULD HAPPEN? IF YOU DON'T TRY, YOU'LL NEVER KNOW IF YOU LIKE IT!

TRY BEING POSITIVE

Concentrate on all the things that make you feel good. Write down five things that always put a smile on your face here:

1 Eating Super Noodles (oviasly) yum

2 doing stuff to do with Merrmaids

3

4

5

STYLE IT OUT

L.O.L. Surprise! girls are never ever slaves to trends. Embrace your own individual style and wear it with pride. The key to looking great is being true to yourself. #superstar style

KEEP GOING

Don't worry if you have a knock-back, just pick yourself up, brush yourself down and try again. If you love something, don't take no for an answer. Work hard and your biggest dreams really can come true.

ROCK OUT WHILE YOU'RE DOING IT

The L.O.L. Surprise! girls are all about sisterhood. Always have your BFFs' backs. Celebrate their successes, and they'll celebrate yours too!

71

L.O.L. PETS...

DOG-PADDLIN' INTO WAVES

YOU'RE INTO L.O.L. PETS IF YOU LIKE......

Fluffy stuff ☐ All kinds of pets ☐
Cuteness ☐ Looking after others ☐

Q. WHAT'S SMALL, CUDDLY AND BRIGHT PURPLE? A. A KOALA HOLDING ITS BREATH!

WHO ARE THE L.O.L. PETS?

Neon Kitty
CLUB: COSPLAY
L.O.L OWNER: NEON Q.T.
WANT ☑ OWN ☐

BATTY 4 U!

Midnight Pup
CLUB: COSPLAY
L.O.L OWNER: MIDNIGHT
WANT ☑ OWN ☐

Hop Hop
CLUB: COSPLAY
L.O.L OWNER: BON BON
WANT ☑ OWN ☐

Fuzzy Fan
CLUB: COSPLAY
L.O.L OWNER: FANIME
WANT ☑ OWN ☑

Heart Barker
CLUB: STORYBOOK
L.O.L OWNER: HEARTBREAKER
WANT ☑ OWN ☐

SQUEAK-A-BOO

Trouble Squeaker
CLUB: STORYBOOK
L.O.L OWNER: TROUBLEMAKER
WANT ☑ OWN ☐

Cottontail Q.T.
CLUB: STORYBOOK
L.O.L OWNER: CURIOUS Q.T.
WANT ☑ OWN ☐

Hops Kit-Tea
CLUB: STORYBOOK
L.O.L OWNER: HOPS
WANT ☑ OWN ☐

WE CAN CHEW IT!

Cherry Ham
CLUB: RETRO
L.O.L OWNER: CHERRY
WANT ☐ OWN ☐

B.B. Pup
CLUB: RETRO
L.O.L OWNER: B.B. BOP
WANT ☐ OWN ☐

Purrr Baby
CLUB: RETRO
L.O.L OWNER: PINK BABY
WANT ☐ OWN ☐

Jitter Critter
CLUB: RETRO
L.O.L OWNER: JITTERBUG
WANT ☐ OWN ☐

I'M BAD TO THE BONE!

M.C. Hammy
CLUB: GLEE
L.O.L OWNER: M.C. SWAG
WANT ☐ OWN ☐

Ruff Rocker
CLUB: GLEE
L.O.L OWNER: ROCKER
WANT ☑ OWN ☐

Bunny Hun
CLUB: HIP HOP
L.O.L OWNER: HONEYBUN
WANT ☑ OWN ☐

D.J. K9
CLUB: HIP HOP
L.O.L OWNER: DJ
WANT ☐ OWN ☑

KICKIN' IT!

Sur-fur Puppy
CLUB: ATHLETIC
L.O.L OWNER: SURFER BABE
WANT ☑ OWN ☐

Rolls
CLUB: ATHLETIC
L.O.L OWNER: SPIKE
WANT ☐ OWN ☐

Roller Kit-10
CLUB: ATHLETIC
L.O.L OWNER: ROLLER SK8TER
WANT ☐ OWN ☐

Hoops D.O.G.G.
CLUB: ATHLETIC
L.O.L OWNER: HOOPS MVP
WANT ☑ OWN ☐

JUST PLAYIN'

Pupsta
CLUB: THEATRE
OWNER: PRANKSTA
WANT ☐ OWN ☐

Baby Dog
CLUB: THEATRE
L.O.L OWNER: BABY CAT
WANT ☐ OWN ✔

Su-Prrr Kitty
CLUB: THEATRE
L.O.L OWNER: SUPER B.B.
WANT ☐ OWN ☐

Bunny Wishes
CLUB: THEATRE
L.O.L OWNER: GENIE
WANT ☐ OWN ☐

It Kitty
CLUB: GLAM
L.O.L OWNER: IT BABY
WANT ☐ OWN ☐

Dollmatian
CLUB: GLAM
L.O.L OWNER: DOLLFACE
WANT ☐ OWN ☐

BEST IN SHOW!

Royal Kitty-Cat
CLUB: GLAM L.O.L OWNER:
ROYAL HIGH-NEY
WANT ☐ OWN ☐

Miss Puppy
CLUB: GLAM
L.O.L OWNER: MISS BABY
WANT ☐ OWN ☐

Kitty Kitty
CLUB: GLITTERATI
L.O.L OWNER: KITTY QUEEN
WANT ✔ OWN ☐

SHE BEE FIERCE!

Pup Bee
CLUB: GLITTERATI
L.O.L OWNER: QUEEN BEE
WANT ☐ OWN ☐

Crystal Bunny
CLUB: GLITTERATI
L.O.L OWNER: CRYSTAL QUEEN
WANT ☐ OWN ☐

Smash Meow-maid
CLUB: GLITTERATI
L.O.L OWNER: SPLASH QUEEN
WANT ✔ OWN ☐

Sugar Pup
CLUB: OPPOSITES
L.O.L OWNER: SUGAR
WANT ☐ OWN ☐

Spicy Kitty
CLUB: OPPOSITES
L.O.L OWNER: SPICE
WANT ☐ OWN ☐

I DON'T WALK.
I GET CARRIED

Fancy Haute Dog
CLUB: OPPOSITES
L.O.L OWNER: FANCY
WANT ☐ OWN ☐

Fresh Feline
CLUB: OPPOSITES
L.O.L OWNER: FRESH
WANT ☐ OWN ☐

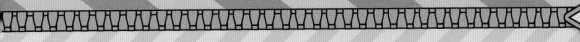

PET WORD BOGGLER

HOW MANY WORDS CAN YOU MAKE, USING THE LETTERS FROM THIS WORD BOGGLER? GIVE YOURSELF A POINT FOR EVERY DOGGY-THEMED WORD!

THEY SEE ME ROLLIN', THEY LOVIN'!

```
K C I T G
E R A S W
N N O B P
L E A D M
```

Write down your words here:

lead
_____

_____

_____

_____

I MADE

_____ WORDS

FIND YOUR IDEAL PET

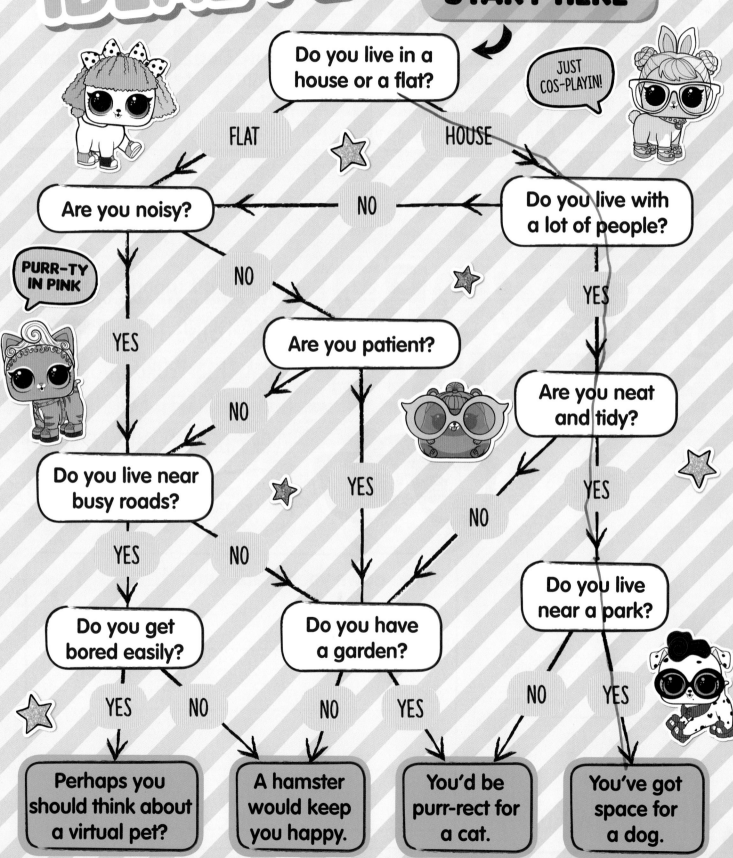

START HERE

Do you live in a house or a flat?

JUST COS-PLAYIN!

FLAT — HOUSE

Do you live with a lot of people?

NO

Are you noisy?

PURR-TY IN PINK

YES

NO

Are you patient?

YES

Are you neat and tidy?

YES

Do you live near busy roads?

YES — NO

NO

YES

Do you live near a park?

Do you get bored easily?

Do you have a garden?

NO — YES

YES — NO

NO — YES

Perhaps you should think about a virtual pet?

A hamster would keep you happy.

You'd be purr-rect for a cat.

You've got space for a dog.

©MGA

PUZZLE ANSWERS

SPACED OUT

CIRCLE EVERY THIRD LETTER IN THIS CODE TO SEE WHAT GLAMSTRONAUT IS LOOKING FORWARD TO. THE FIRST LETTER IS CIRCLED FOR YOU.

W E ⓒ O R ⓞ J U Ⓓ Y I N Ⓗ N R
F G ⒺR P Y G ⒶJ H R ⒺF T Y ⓉY

GLAMSTRONAUT IS LOOKING FORWARD TO A....... C O D I N G   P A R T Y

PASSWORD PICKER

CROSS OUT ALL THE LETTERS THAT APPEAR MORE THAN TWICE. THEN UNSCRAMBLE THE CODE TO REVEAL THE WIFI PASSWORD.

The password is
S U R P R I S E

COOL CODE CHALLENGE

There are more
ONES (20X1 16X0)

WORD WHIZZ

Can you spot the words hidden in this word search?

CHEER   CLAP   DANCE   FRIENDS

U	P	R	S	R	P	C	E	C	D
C	N	E	F	D	O	C	L	U	V
I	H	E	E	X	N	P	G	A	O
L	H	H	K	A	Q	E	V	R	P
B	J	C	D	S	V	D	I	X	H
T	P	W	F	U	Q	Y	C	R	F
H	L	J	F	D	P	B	Y	S	F
P	B	A	I	G	Q	B	H	Q	B
C	H	A	N	T	N	A	E	N	C
T	Y	L	U	K	C	X	T	O	S

The surprise word is
C H A N T

SPARKLY SWIRL

FIND THE WORDS

G	N	O	Y	I	X	W	T	X	L	J	X	U
C	N	Z	W	Q	N	Z	G	T	S	B	D	V
I	X	I	V	D	K	W	R	U	M	X	C	G
V	R	N	M	I	A	G	N	G	B	O	N	X
G	Z	K	F	M	W	F	G	N	X	R	Z	V
O	G	S	D	F	I	N	V	I	U	Z	X	L
W	Z	E	Z	P	I	W	G	P	K	O	L	Z
M	Q	H	N	N	A	Z	S	P	U	Q	E	F
H	A	L	N	F	Y	C	E	I	I	A	A	O
G	J	U	V	O	K	E	K	T	C	W	I	
T	R	K	C	Q	X	Q	N	S	H	N	M	X
N	Z	B	V	F	Y	D	Q	R	V	V	X	Z
V	J	U	F	X	E	T	J	I	F	U	G	E

The missing word is
G Y M N A S T I C S

SPORTY TREASURE HUNT

Your surprise challenge is to set up a game of

F O O T B A L L

with your friends

©MGA